How To Draw
CARTOON CHARACTERS

Illustrations by John Newall
Cover illustrations by John Newall & Greg C Grace

ISBN: 1 86476 274 8

Copyright © Axiom Publishing, 2004.
Unit 2, 1 Union Street, Stepney, South Australia, 5069.

This edition for
SELECT EDITIONS
Devizes
Wiltshire, UK

Printed in Malaysia

How to draw cartoon characters

ACROBAT

STEP 1:
Using a pencil begin by drawing the circles and lines matching where they fit into the squares.

STEP 2:
With a black pen and following the rough shapes and lines, draw the outline shape.

STEP 3:
Rub out pencil lines.

STEP 4:
Shade in and colour.

OBSERVATION DETAILS:
Leaving a white highlight on the pupil of the eye is a popular way of giving the eyes a more lively appearance.

FIREMAN

STEP 1:
Using a pencil begin by drawing the circles and lines matching where they fit into the squares.

STEP 2:
With a black pen and following the rough shapes and lines, draw the outline shape.

STEP 3:
Rub out pencil lines.

STEP 4:
Shade in and colour.

How to draw cartoon characters

OBSERVATION DETAILS:
When adding shading to the character, keep in mind the light source. Shading has been applied as parallel lines here but there is many other ways to create tone, such as dots or watered down ink applied with a brush.

How to draw cartoon characters

OFFICE WORKER

Using a pencil begin by drawing the circles and lines matching where they fit into the squares.

With a black pen and following the rough shapes and lines, draw the outline shape.

Rub out pencil lines.

Shade in and colour.

How to draw cartoon characters

OBSERVATION DETAILS:
Dark/ black objects can be tricky to shade. Parallel lines can be used to create a dark tone (used on the suit) or the object can be filled in with black leaving white highlights (used on the hair)

DRESS UP

STEP 1:
Using a pencil begin by drawing the circles and lines matching where they fit into the squares.

STEP 2:
With a black pen and following the rough shapes and lines, draw the outline shape.

STEP 3:
Rub out pencil lines.

STEP 4:
Shade in and colour.

How to draw cartoon characters

OBSERVATION DETAILS:
Pay attention to how the bandages curve around the body to help describe the volume of the body.

How to draw cartoon characters

FISHING

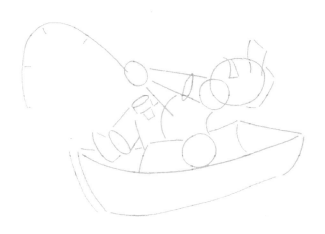

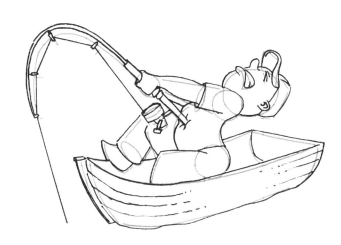

STEP 1:
Using a pencil begin by drawing the circles and lines matching where they fit into the squares.

STEP 2:
With a black pen and following the rough shapes and lines, draw the outline shape.

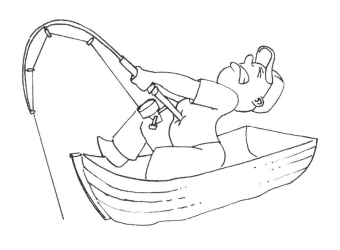

STEP 3:
Rub out pencil lines.

STEP 4:
Shade in and colour.

How to draw cartoon characters

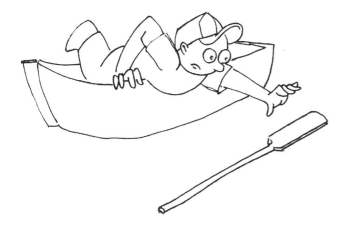

OBSERVATION DETAILS:
Cartoons allow greatly exaggerated poses, situations and facial expressions. Have fun with the subjet.

How to draw cartoon characters

CATCH

STEP 1:
Using a pencil begin by drawing the circles and lines matching where they fit into the squares.

STEP 2:
With a black pen and following the rough shapes and lines, draw the outline shape.

STEP 3:
Rub out pencil lines.

STEP 4:
Shade in and colour.

How to draw cartoon characters

OBSERVATION DETAILS:
Facial expressions are an important aspect of cartooning. Start each face with the position of the eyes and use them as a guide for positioning the other features.

How to draw cartoon characters

HANDYMAN

STEP 1:

Using a pencil begin by drawing the circles and lines matching where they fit into the squares.

STEP 2:

With a black pen and following the rough shapes and lines, draw the outline shape.

STEP 3:

Rub out pencil lines.

STEP 4:

Shade in and colour.

How to draw cartoon characters

OBSERVATION DETAILS:
Keep in mind physical characteristics of your people—in this case the man has a bulging, muscular frame. Make sure you capture this look.

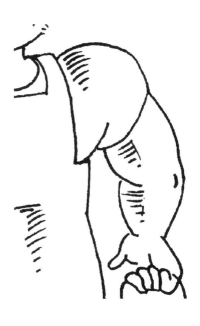

How to draw cartoon characters

DOCTOR

STEP 1:

Using a pencil begin by drawing the circles and lines matching where they fit into the squares.

STEP 2:

With a black pen and following the rough shapes and lines, draw the outline shape.

STEP 3:

Rub out pencil lines.

STEP 4:

Shade in and colour.

OBSERVATION DETAILS:
Cartoon characters often have relatively large heads compared to their bodies. Don't be afraid to distort the proportions of your characters to add comical value.

How to draw cartoon characters

SKIER

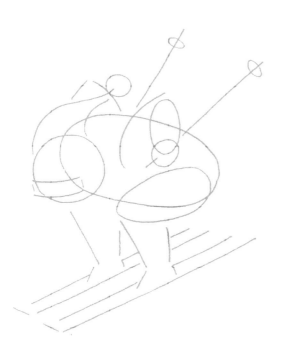

STEP 1:
Using a pencil begin by drawing the circles and lines matching where they fit into the squares.

STEP 2:
With a black pen and following the rough shapes and lines, draw the outline shape.

STEP 3:
Rub out pencil lines.

STEP 4:
Shade in and colour.

How to draw cartoon characters

OBSERVATION DETAILS:
Traditionally cartoonists used ink and dip pens, but modern cartoonists often experiment with different media. The cartoons I drew in this book were done with a felt tip pen but I also use brushes and even sticks! Experiment to see what suits you.

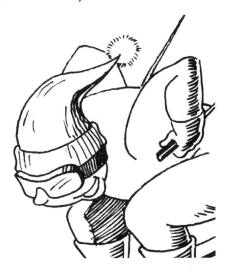

How to draw cartoon characters

SNORKELLING

STEP 1:
Using a pencil begin by drawing the circles and lines matching where they fit into the squares.

STEP 2:
With a black pen and following the rough shapes and lines, draw the outline shape.

STEP 3:
Rub out pencil lines.

STEP 4:
Shade in and colour.

OBSERVATION DETAILS:
Remember that hair floats around in water. Details like this help create the impression of being underwater, as do the bubbles.

MUSICIAN

STEP 1:
Using a pencil begin by drawing the circles and lines matching where they fit into the squares.

STEP 2:
With a black pen and following the rough shapes and lines, draw the outline shape.

STEP 3:
Rub out pencil lines.

STEP 4:
Shade in and colour.

How to draw cartoon characters

OBSERVATION DETAILS:
Adding a shadow on the ground can help indicate that your character is in the air. The further the character is from the shadow, the higher above that ground they will appear.

How to draw cartoon characters

SKIPPING

STEP 1:
Using a pencil begin by drawing the circles and lines matching where they fit into the squares.

STEP 2:
With a black pen and following the rough shapes and lines, draw the outline shape.

STEP 3:
Rub out pencil lines.

STEP 4:
Shade in and colour.

How to draw cartoon characters

OBSERVATION DETAILS:
I usually describe feet and shoes with simple shapes. Cartoonists often simplify their subject matter, this allows them to concentrate on capturing the essence of the message they want to communicate.

SOCCER PLAYER

STEP 1:
Using a pencil begin by drawing the circles and lines matching where they fit into the squares.

STEP 2:
With a black pen and following the rough shapes and lines, draw the outline shape.

STEP 3:
Rub out pencil lines.

STEP 4:
Shade in and colour.

How to draw cartoon characters

OBSERVATION DETAILS:
Don't be afraid to add 'motion lines' to help indicate what action is occurring. These lines and marks can take any form that helps describes the action, and their use is only limited by your imagination.

How to draw cartoon characters

TENNIS PLAYER

STEP 1:
Using a pencil begin by drawing the circles and lines matching where they fit into the squares.

STEP 2:
With a black pen and following the rough shapes and lines, draw the outline shape.

STEP 3:
Rub out pencil lines.

STEP 4:
Shade in and colour.

How to draw cartoon characters

OBSERVATION DETAILS:
The ball has been drawn larger than it really is, this creates the appearance that it is travelling forward and is closer than the tennis player.

How to draw cartoon characters

Draw your own cartoon character

STEP 1:
Using a pencil begin by drawing the circles and lines matching where they fit into the squares.

STEP 2:
With a black pen and following the rough shapes and lines, draw the outline shape.

STEP 3:
Rub out pencil lines.

STEP 4:
Shade in and colour.